MADAGASCAR 3

JOKE BOOK

BANTAM BOOKS

MADAGASCAR 3: JOKE BOOK
A BANTAM BOOK 978 0 857 51136 2

Published in Great Britain by Bantam,
an imprint of Random House Children's Publishers UK
A Random House Group Company.

This edition published 2012

1 3 5 7 9 10 8 6 4 2

Madagascar 3 © 2012 DreamWorks Animation L.L.C.

Written and designed by Dan Newman.

Bantam Books are published by Random House Children's Publishers UK,
61–63 Uxbridge Road, London W5 5SA

www.**randomhousechildrens**.co.uk

Addresses for companies within
The Random House Group Limited can be found at:
www.randomhouse.co.uk/offices.htm

THE RANDOM HOUSE GROUP Limited Reg. No. 954009

A CIP catalogue record for this book is available from the British Library

Printed and bound by CPI Group (UK) Ltd, Croydon, CR0 4YY

The Random House Group Limited supports The Forest Stewardship Council
(FSC), the leading international forest certification organization.
Our books carrying the FSC label are printed on FSC®-certified paper.
FSC is the only forest certification scheme endorsed by the leading
environmental organizations, including Greenpeace. Our paper procurement
policy can be found at www.randomhouse.co.uk/environment

CONTENTS

WELCOME TO...

CIRCUS ZARAGOZA

A
PERFORMANCE
YOU WILL
NEVER
FORGET!

The elephants

Jonesy

Circus dogs

Phil and Mason

Kowalski and Skipper

Private and Rico

King Julien and Mort

Maurice

Marty and Alex

Gia

Melman

Vitaly

Gloria

Stefano

Sonya

Esmarelda, Ernstina and Esperanza

5

ALL ABOUT ALEX

What do you call Alex wearing
a ringmaster's hat?
A dandy-lion.

Stefano offered Alex a nice meal
in return for all his help with
the circus.
　'Would you like a starter?' he asked.
　'Some sushi would be nice, thanks,'
replied Alex.
　'And what would you like for
your main?'
　'A brush and a comb, please.'

What's Alex's favourite ice cream?
Roar-sberry ripple.

Alex's mane was getting long, so he had a hair cut.
Tomorrow he might get the rest of them cut too.

Vitaly has started teaching Alex
how to lift weights.
He's beginning to pick it up.

6

Gia was very nervous about swinging high up in the air. Especially as Alex made it look so trap-ezey.

Gia managed to do everything that Alex did. **She's a copy-cat.**

One of the circus cars was completely lined with mirrors. Alex asked if he could have it — he could really see himself living there.

Vitaly asked Alex to watch while he stuck a knife into the wall, but Alex couldn't see the point.

ALEX'S FAVOURITE FILMS:

The Sound of Mew-sic

Roar-ders of the Lost Ark

Mission Im-paws-ible

Hairy Potter and the Goblet of Fur

Transformers: Dark of the Mane

Mary Paw-pins

Prince of Purr-sia

Mane in Black

Alex has heard that some of his ancestors performed at the Colosseum in Rome with some human captives, but didn't do very well.

Apparently the humans went down a treat and the lions got fed up.

Lousy Limericks

The small dancing dogs
  are the tops
They prance with a series
  of hops
Till one had to scratch
An embarrassing patch
And the audience yelled
  'Call the cops!'

Stefano wishes one thing:
To be known as the Juggling King.
But some nights he falls,
Or swallows the balls,
Or trips and rolls out of the ring.

Sonya the bicycling bear
Is huge and covered with hair.
She grumbles and growls,
Bares her teeth when she howls
But Julien loves her — so there!

Gia's a beautiful cat
And rather a good acrobat.
She grabs the trapeze
With the greatest of ease
And hardly ever falls flat.

The horses have feathers and bells
Their act causes cheers and yells
They're great in the ring
But there's just one thing
That's not good – the terrible smells!

Dubois is hot on the trail
Of Alex's long fluffy tail.
She thinks that it's fine
To hunt this poor lion –
Let's hope she'll finally fail!

SORT THE
Silhouette

Alex loves showing off to a crowd. But which of these shadows is the right one for this spectacular pose?

A

B

C

D

E

ANIMAL ANAGRAMS

Circus Zaragoza is home to many wild creatures. Can you unravel these anagrams to discover ten different animals?

PLANET EH

ERGIT

URAGAJ

ACME HEN ZIP

IS ALONE

REBA

MISHAP POP OUT

BRAZE

I GAFFER

EL RUM

Answers on page 94

SUPER VITALY

Why didn't Vitaly bite the clowns?
He thought they tasted funny.

Why is Vitaly so fast?
Because he's Russian.

Vitaly won't use a blunt knife
in his knife-throwing act.
There's no point.

Why is a shellfish seller like Vitaly?
They both have bags of mussels.

What are Vitaly's favourite sweets?
Extra-strong mints.

Alex: 'So, you're from Russia, Vitaly?
       Which part?'
Vitaly: 'All of me.'

Vitaly is so strong, he can squeeze orange juice with his bare paws ... from bananas.

Vitaly did 100 pull-ups yesterday. **He needs to get a better belt.**

'Gloria, you know I'll never find another hippo like you.'
'That's sweet, honey. But I hope you haven't been looking to check!'

What game is Gloria good at?
SQUASH.

'Melman, do you think I'm vain?'
'Not at all, honey. Why do you ask?'
'Well, most girls as gorgeous as me are usually vain.'

Why would Gloria make a good pirate?
She's already got plenty of booty.

'Oh Gloria, I wish I could dance like this with you forever!'
'What – you don't want to improve?'

What happened when
Gloria ate a bag of garlic?
**Her bark was definitely worse than
her bite.**

**What did Gloria do
before learning to
walk the tightrope?
She ate a well-
balanced meal.**

What's
Gloria's
favourite
music?
Hippo-hop.

CIRCUS FUNNIES

How do you make a small
fortune from a circus?
Start with a large fortune.

Why are circus performers
good artists?
Because they can draw a crowd.

What goes OOHC OOHC?
The circus train going backwards.

What's a twack?
**A twack is what the circus twain
wides on.**

How did the Zoosters feel when
they got on the circus train?
Chuffed.

What's big, grey and
doesn't matter?
An irr-elephant.

What do you call the elephants when they're riding on the circus train?
Passengers.

What do the elephants have for lunch?
One hour, the same as everyone else.

How do the elephants keep in touch?
They call each other on the elephone.

MAINLY MARTY

'Marty,' asked Alex. 'Do you ever exaggerate?'
  'Never,' replied Marty. 'Never, ever, ever.'

'Hey, Marty — do you know what 'coincidence' means?'
  'That's weird — I was just about to ask you exactly the same thing.'

Marty was very nervous about being fired out of a cannon, but he gave it his best shot.

Stefano: 'I have to do all the odd jobs for the circus, but I'm not a good electrician.'

Marty: 'That's shocking.'

Marty's about to do his act when he realizes that an Englishman, a Frenchman, a Spaniard and a German in the audience can't see him properly.
    He climbs up higher and calls out, 'Can you all see me now?'
    'Yes.'
    'Oui.'
    'Sí.'
    'Ja.'

What always makes Marty smile? The muscles either side of his mouth.

Stefano: 'Marty, do you mind what job you do at the circus?'

Marty: 'No, I'm flexible.'

Stefano: 'Great — you can be our new contortionist, then.'

WHAT ARE MARTY'S FAVOURITE MOVIES? OLD ONES ... IN BLACK AND WHITE.

Marty helped Stefano tidy up a big pile of empty food sacks and he did a really good job.
He's crackalackin' at stackin' sackin'.

MARTY'S GOOD ADVICE

**If you can't see the bright side of life,
polish the dull side.**

Always speak well of your enemies –
after all, you made them.

**When you're arguing with an idiot, make
sure they're not doing the same thing.**

The bigger the itch, the less chance
you have of being able to reach it.

**If you can't laugh at yourself,
someone else will do it for you.**

You can't change the wind,
but you can adjust your sails.

**You can fool some of the people
some of the time, and that's enough.**

If you tell the truth, you don't have to
remember what you said.

**Friends are like teabags. You don't know
how good they are until they're in hot water.**

Two wrongs don't make a right.
But three rights make a left.

SPOT THE DIFFERENCE

Can you find ten differences between these two pictures?

Mark them on the picture above, then check your answers on page 94.

How do you smarten up creased seals?
Use a seal-iron.

Where does Stefano like to watch movies?
At the dive-in.

Stefano struggled to balance
on a big ball, but with
practise he got good enough
to do it every time.
He was on a roll.

Why does Stefano like to swim
in salt water?
Because pepper water makes him sneeze.

Stefano gets pretty tired
playing the horns.
**Last night he was
completely parped.**

Did you know sealions can't watch just
one TV show - they have to keep changing
channels all the time.
Big flippers, sealions.

Stefano didn't think he was much good as a sealion cannonball. **He kept getting fired.**

He was persuaded to keep at it though — he was the right caliber for the job.

Stefano likes to have the final say on whether an act is good enough for the circus. He's the seal of approval.

MONKEYING ABOUT
WITH PHIL AND MASON

Phil can only remember 25
letters of the alphabet.
He doesn't know why.

Marty saw Mason carrying a tin opener.
Laughing, he yelled, 'You don't need a tin
opener to open a banana!'
  'I know,' replied Mason. 'This is for the
custard.'

'Mason, stop pulling Gia's tail!'
  'I'm not pulling, Alex, I'm holding.
She's doing all the pulling.'

What kind of stories do
Phil and Mason like best?
Furry tales.

What was the first thing Phil learned to read?
Ape-B-C.

What do monkeys love to eat?
Chocolate chimp cookies.

Why do apes wear sunscreen?
To get a nice orangu-tan.

What's a monkey's favourite month?
Ape-ril.

How do monkeys make toast?
They put a slice of bread under a gorilla.

29

ODD ANIMAL OUT

In each of these four groups, one picture is different from the others. Can you spot them?

30

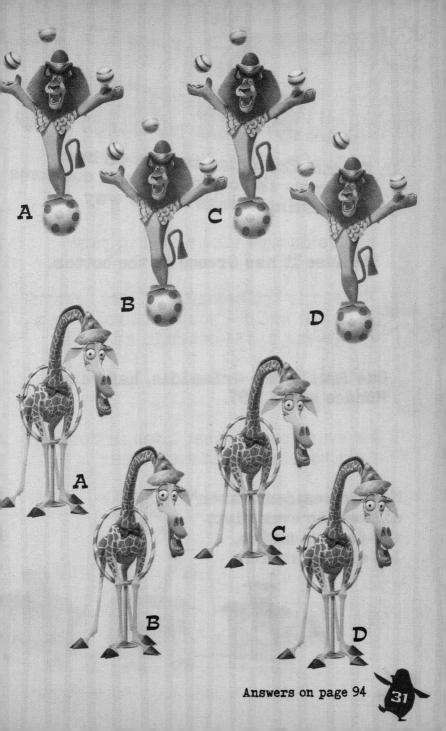

A

B

C

D

A

B

C

D

Answers on page 94

FUN FACTS

Circus Zaragoza travels all over Europe – the animals found out some interesting things on the way . . .

Why is Europe like a frying pan?
Because it has Greece at the bottom.

Monaco is the second smallest country in the world – you could walk from one end to the other in an hour.

One family, the Grimaldis, has ruled Monaco since 1297.

For every person that lives in Monaco, eight tourists visit every year.

Monaco residents aren't allowed to even visit the famous casino, let alone gamble.

For its size, Monaco has more millionaires and billionaires than anywhere else in the world.

It's lucky the Monkey-plane can hover — there isn't room for an airport in Monaco.

Marty likes two boiled eggs for breakfast, except when he's in France. That's because in France one egg is un ouef.

The Alps are over 1,000km long and run through seven countries — Slovenia, Austria, Italy, Switzerland, Liechtenstein, Germany and France.

The highest mountain in the Alps is Mont Blanc in France — 4,808m high.

Melman Madness

Melman's been so happy since meeting Gloria that he feels he could live forever.
So far, so good.

What are Melman's favourite stories?
Tall tales.

'Gloria, it really pains me to say this . . .'
    'What, Melman?'
    'I've got a really sore throat.'

What's the smartest thing Melman can say?
'Gloria says . . .'

What does Melman always know before anyone else?
If it's started raining.

34

How did Melman get a headache?
Looking through a venetian blind at Marty and the Penguins walking over a zebra crossing.

Melman fell into a deep, dark hole.
He couldn't see that well.

'Gloria, why do you want me to put fruit in the microwave?'
'I didn't say that, honey — I said I wanted a hot date.'

Melman's mouthwash says it kills 99.9% of all germs.
Which means his mouth is full of dead germs.

Melman was panicking on the tightrope, so Gloria shouted some advice.
'Whatever you do, honey — don't look down!'
So Melman started smiling.

Before he left Africa and joined the circus, Melman was very popular giving medical advice to the other giraffes ...

'Doctor Melman, I've hurt my leg in two places.'
'Well, don't go back to those places, then.'

'Doctor Melman, you've got to help me out!'
'Sure. Which way did you come in?'

'Doctor Melman, I've just been beaten up by an enormous insect!'
'You're the fourth giraffe today to say that. There must be a nasty bug going around.'

'Doctor Melman, I've got a bad head cold. How can I stop it reaching my chest?'
'Tie a knot in your neck.'

MELMAN'S LATEST FEARS

Claustrophobia – fear of Father Christmas

Anoraknophobia – fear of spiders wearing waterproof coats

Aggrophobia – fear of seeing a fight outdoors

Acropophobia – fear of standing on top of Greek monuments

Phobophobia – fear of being frightened

Xenophobia – fear of strange letters of the alphabet

Hydroburpia – fear of fizzy water

37

WHAT'S MY NAME?

Marty

Melman

Julien

Gia

Gloria

Stefano

The names of these characters need to be put into this grid. Can you work out how to fit them all in?

Alex

Vitaly

Answer on page 95

SILLY CIRCUS

What cheers up a sick elephant?
A Get Wellephant card.

How do you get four elephants
in a clown car?
Two in the front, two in the back.

How does
Gloria get in
the clown car?
She asks one
of the elephants to
get out.

Why don't the elephants
ride bicycles?
Because they don't have
any thumbs to ring the
bell with.

What's beautiful,
grey and wears
glass slippers?
Cinderelephant.

SIGNS YOU'RE IN A BAD CIRCUS

The dust is so thick,
the cockroaches are on stilts.

The tigers have zips up their backs.

There's only one dancing dog,
and she's so thin . . .
she's wearing a one-one.

**It's so dirty, you wipe your feet
on the mat when you leave.**

The circus ring is a hula hoop.

**Even the elephants have forgotten
when they last heard a cheer.**

The tightrope act is run on a shoestring.

GORGEOUS GIA

Gia dreamt that someone was shouting
'On your marks, get set, go!' at her.
She woke up with a start.

**What does Gia always get on
her birthday?
Another year older.**

Where was Gia when the light went out?
In the dark.

Why is it hard for Gia to play
hide-and-seek?
Because she's always spotted.

Where could you find Gia a nice
present?
From a cat-alogue.

Can Gia juggle?
PAWSIBLY.

Does Gia always get her own way?
Yes – she's very purr-suasive.

What does Gia
on a beach have
in common with
Christmas?
Sandy Claws.

43

'Maurice, I want a blackboard and a few rows of desks in our room.'
'Really? What for?'
'To make it classy.'

'Do you know what I love doing more than anything else, Maurice? Trying to pack myself into a small suitcase. Oh, I love it! I can hardly contain myself.'

'Maurice, I think I can lift an elephant with only one paw.'
'Really, sir? That would be amazing to watch.'
'Would it? Then bring me a one-pawed elephant.'

Julien dreamed that he had eaten his own tail and leg in the night. **He woke up feeling pretty full of himself.**

Julien loved Sonya, but he told her he was disappointed about her lack of vocabulary. **She was lost for words.**

Julien took Sonya window-shopping in Rome. They bought seven windows.

When Sonya showed Julien the beautiful sights of Italy's capital city, he turned into an old table. **He's such a Rome-antique.**

Julien and Sonya were hungry as they toured round Rome, but all the restaurants and shops were shut. What did Julien say when they found a big, round Margarita lying in the road?

'That's a pizza luck!'

Pick a Penguin!

Private

Skipper

Kowalski

Rico

46

The Penguins are helping to put up the circus tent. But only one of them is holding a rope leading to the big top – which one?

Answer on page 95

GLORIOUS GLORIA

Gloria's trying the seafood diet.
When she sees food, she eats it.

Gloria tries not to point out Melman's faults.
She doesn't want to be hippo-critical.

**Why was Gloria standing in front of a mirror with her eyes closed?
She was checking on something –
Melman had told her that she looked beautiful when she was asleep . . .**

How does Gloria get Melman to do whatever she wants?
She uses hipponotism.

**Melman told Gloria she had drawn her eyebrows on too high.
She looked pretty surprised.**

Gloria was hoping to look good on the tightrope, but she slipped and fell onto the safety net. However, she made a big impression, and she soon bounced back!

What's the best way to remember Gloria's birthday?
Forget it once. She'll make sure you never forget again!

Gloria passed out after eating too much curry.
She fell into a korma.

Gloria can't wait to start ballet dancing.
She wants to get straight to the pointe.

Gloria wanted to make a ballet skirt, but she wasn't sure how to start.
Then she put tu and tu together.

GLORIA'S FAVOURITE FOODS

Hippopota-mousse

**Mississippi Mud Pie
(with extra mud)**

Fish and chippos

Hippotato waffles

Miracle Whippo

Chocolate chippo cookies

Gloria has heard about a
new Chinese diet.
You can eat as much as you like,
but you can only use one chopstick.

WACKY
WORDSEARCH

Can you find all of these words in the grid? They may run up, down, forwards or backwards but not diagonally.

CIRCUS
ACROBAT
JUGGLER
BIG TOP
ZARAGOZA
CLOWN
MONACO
COLOSSEUM
LONDON
ROME
TRAIN

A	N	N	C	R	O	O	N	L	O
C	W	U	U	C	A	Z	O	Z	T
P	O	T	G	I	B	A	D	L	A
A	L	O	B	R	C	R	N	O	B
G	C	R	R	C	O	A	O	S	O
C	E	R	J	U	G	G	L	E	R
N	M	U	E	S	S	O	L	O	C
G	O	S	N	B	R	Z	E	L	A
O	R	L	M	O	N	A	C	O	C
L	N	I	A	R	T	S	O	M	M

Answer on page 95

DARLING DANCING DOGS

Freddie: 'I'm worried my legs are too short for dancing.'

Jonesy: 'Don't be silly, they're fine! They all reach the ground, don't they?'

How many dancing dogs does it take to change a lightbulb?
'Ah-one, two, one-two-three-four . . .'

Alex: 'Those dogs are amazing dancers!'

Gia: 'Aren't they? Especially when you think they've all got two left feet.'

One of the dogs went missing. Stefano wasn't sure what to do so he put an advert in the local paper saying, 'Here boy!'

Why do the dogs run round in circles?
Well, have you ever tried running in squares?

Jonesy: 'Meow . . . meow, meow. Meow.'
Shakes: 'What on earth are you doing?'
Jonesy: 'Learning a foreign language.'

What has a tail, eight wheels and makes a noise like a cat?
Jonesy on jet-propelled roller skates . . .
'Meeeeeyoooooowww!'

Why did the dancing dogs have to give up tap dancing?
They kept falling in the sink.

PESKY PENGUINS

The Penguins were trying to cross a busy road, but the traffic was so heavy they couldn't get across. A bear walking by said to them, 'If it's any help, there's a zebra crossing just down the road.'

'Really?' replied Skipper. 'I hope he's having better luck than we are.'

What's black and white and goes up, down, up, down?
Private on Julien's bouncy castle.

56

Where do the Penguins keep their money?
In a snow bank.

Why are the Penguins so brave?
Because they're totally furless.

Why did Private cross the road?
He was impersonating a chicken.

What did Skipper call Rico when he crossed the road, rolled in the dirt and came back again?
'A dirty double-crosser.'

What's black and white and red?
A sunburnt penguin.

Skipper came back to the Penguins' room
and found it was in a terrible mess.
'This place is in a state! Which one
of you is responsible?' he yelled.
'None of us, boss,' replied Kowalski.
'We're all irresponsible. That's why
it's a mess.'

What do you call a penguin with no eyes?
A PENGUN.

57

JOIN THE DOTS

What is Marty so happy to be in? Join dots 1 to 25 to find out.

58

WORD GRID

Fill in the names across the grid to reveal another name in the highlighted squares, reading down.

1				A				
2								I
3	R							
4							E	
5				L				
6		P						
7	M							

Need help? Look back at page 4!

Answers on page 96

DANGEROUS

Dubois isn't as mean as everyone says she is. **She's actually much, much worse.**

Dubois is very keen on preserving endangered animals . . . She makes jam out of pandas.

Dubois has a huge stuffed animal head right over her desk.

'That's pretty impressive,' said one of her assistants.

'I'm not so sure,' replied Dubois. 'That thing almost killed me.'

'Really? Did it attack you?'

'No, it fell off the wall and landed on my head.'

Dubois found the perfect way to follow the circus train. **She used a search engine.**

DUBOIS

Dubois is keen to catch all the Zoosters, but she really wants to nab Alex. **He's the mane attraction.**

You know how you always find something in the last place you look? Dubois is so good, she finds it in the FIRST place she looks.

Dubois and her men found a set of tracks and she decided to test them.

'What kind of tracks are these?' she asked.

'Lion tracks, I think,' said one assistant.

'No, giraffe tracks,' said another.

'Definitely hippo tracks,' said a third.

'Make up your mind,' sighed Dubois. 'There's a train coming.'

Dubois always manages to follow the trail of every animal she hunts. She's got an excellent track record.

MONKEY MAYHEM

Why do chimps have big nostrils?
Because they've got big fingers.

Why does Phil keep scratching himself?
Because no-one else knows where he itches.

Phil and Mason had to count the circus takings, so Mason asked Stefano if he had a calculator.
'Sorry, no,' said Stefano. 'Only this broken abacus.'
Mason sighed. 'That doesn't count.'

What line of work are Phil and Mason in?
Monkey business.

Mason is very like his father.
He's a chimp off the old block.

When they were in Monaco, Phil and Mason kept going to the harbour and sailing boats that weren't theirs. They've never really understood the idea of 'own a ship'.

WHAT DO YOU CALL A MONKEY WITH ONE LEG? A WONKEY.

Phil and Mason won so much money in the casino, they struggled to find ways to spend it. One day was brilliant — they bought dozens and dozens of bouncy castles, blew them all up and spent the whole day bouncing.

However, the next day was just a huge let down.

How do you fix a broken chimpanzee?
With a monkey wrench.

Phil may not talk, but he thinks a lot.
Here are some of the things
he thinks about . . .

**If someone from Poland is a Pole, shouldn't
someone from Holland be a Hole?**

*If you try your hardest to fail, but actually
succeed, what have you done?*

**They know the speed of light,
but what's the speed of dark?**

*If you expect the unexpected, won't that make
the unexpected become expected?*

**If a dictionary had a word in that was spelt
wrong, how would anyone know?**

*If clouds and rain are both made of water,
why do clouds stay up in the air while rain
falls to the ground?*

**How can you tell when you've run out
of invisible ink?**

Do history exams get harder every year?

Why do all old ladies have the same haircut?

MORE FUN FACTS

There's a phrase that says, 'Rome wasn't built in a day.'
Does that mean it was built at night?

Every Italian eats 30 kilos of pasta every year. That's a lot of spaghetti!

The symbol of Rome is twin baby boys being mothered by a wolf.

Things that are unlucky in Italy: dropping salt; wearing purple to the theatre; having 13 people sit down to dinner; putting a hat on a bed.

In Lazio, Italy, the police drive Lamborghini sports cars.

The thermometer, the typewriter and the piano are all Italian inventions.

Italy has three active volcanoes. Don't tell King Julien!

LONDON IS THE **BIGGEST** CITY IN EUROPE.

There are more languages spoken in London than any other city in the world.

London was the first city anywhere to have an underground railway.

London is the only city to have hosted the Olympic Games three times.

MONACO MAZE

Can you guide the Zoosters across town without meeting Chantel Dubois?

Pick a Pair

Join the pairs of words that go together. The first pair has been done for you.

BIG   DOG

SAFETY   MAN

JUGGLING   MASTER

TRAPEZE   EATER

TIGHT   THROWER

RING   ROPE

FIRE   BALL

DANCING   BAR

STRONG   TOP

KNIFE   NET

Answers on page 96

HEY HEY, IT'S THE HORSES

Esmarelda will only perform in the dark.
She's a night mare.

Her sisters, Esperanza and Ernstina, are much easier to deal with.
They're stable creatures.

You need to be careful putting on their saddles though – you don't want to stirrup trouble.

How did Esmarelda shrink?
She caught a cough, and became a little hoarse.

Did she recover?
Yes – she took some cough stirrup.

Esperanza got sick next – she caught hay fever.
So she went to horse-pital.

The horses have travelled everywhere with the circus.
They're globe-trotters.

Why did Stefano stand behind the horses?
He thought he might get a kick out of it.

The horses get on well when they sleep
next to each other.
They're good neigh-bours.

MORE MELMAN MADNESS

Melman came home one day covered in bruises. He had started to go through a revolving door and changed his mind.

Melman fell off a ten-metre-tall ladder, but he wasn't hurt. He fell off the bottom rung.

What's the difference between a thunderstorm and Melman with a tiny bruise?
One pours with rain, the other roars with pain.

Melman complained to Gloria that he was hurting all over his body.

'Really?' she said. 'Show me what you mean.'

Melman touched one knee and yelled, 'Ouch, that hurts!' He touched his stomach and groaned, 'Oww-ow-ow!' Then he touched his ear. 'Ouch, even that hurts!'

'I think I know what the problem is, honey,' said Gloria. 'You've broken your hoof.'

I'm not saying Melman is a pessimist, but he looks both ways when he crosses a one-way street.

Melman became frightened of two-letter words.
He got scared just thinking about it.

'Oh honey, did that bee sting you? We'd better put some cream on it.'
'Don't be silly, Gloria – it'll be miles away by now.'

What kind of car does Melman prefer?
A stretch limousine.

JIGSAW JUGGLE

Which pieces go where in this jigsaw? And which piece doesn't fit anywhere in the puzzle?

74

Answers on page 96

King Julien AND THE LEMURS

'Can you help me with this jigsaw puzzle, Maurice? It's really hard – I can't even find any edge pieces.'

'What's the puzzle of, Mort?'

'A big chicken eating breakfast.'

'That's not a puzzle, silly. Now let's put the cornflakes back.'

Mort stayed up all night once, wondering where the sun went. Eventually it dawned on him.

Mort always sleeps like a baby.
He wakes up crying every two hours.

Maurice can make his own fireworks. He's got a flare for it.

'Maurice, have you started answering every question with another question?'

'Why do you ask?'

Mort is really interested in magnets. Maurice can't see the attraction.

'Mort, please
be quiet.
Don't you know
it's rude to
talk when I'm
interrupting?'

'Maurice, I
have invented
a lucky knife
that can cut four
loaves of bread at once.'
  'Sounds great, your
majesty. What do you
call it?'
  'A four-loaf cleaver.'

QUESTIONS KING JULIEN WANTS ANSWERED

Why doesn't glue stick
to the inside of the bottle?

**What sticks the non-stick coating
on to non-stick pans?**

What do farmers plant when they
want to grow seedless grapes?

**Why do they put lifejackets under
the seats in planes, not parachutes?**

Would the ocean be deeper
if it didn't have sponges in it?

**How do the 'Keep Off The Grass'
signs get there?**

Where can you throw away
a broken rubbish bin?

**What was the best thing before
sliced bread?**

CLOWNING AROUND

Now that Circus Zaragoza is all-animal, they like to tell jokes about how silly the clowns were ...

Whenever they reached a new town, every clown would wash and dry his costume, and then iron it on a windowsill. This was because they'd heard the phrase 'every clown has a sill for ironing.'

A clown spent ages making himself a belt for his costume, made entirely out of herbs – and never wore it.
It was a complete waist of thyme.

Another clown got fed up with having to write his name in his outfits, so he changed his name to 'Machine Washable.'

Two clowns were arguing about how tall the Big Top was. The ringmaster suggested that next time they took down the tent, they could lay the main pole on the ground and measure it.
'That's no good,' replied a clown. 'We want to know how tall it is, not how long.'

One of the clowns started stealing paint from the circus.
He was caught red-handed.

The clowns had some useless musical instruments, including a broken drum. You can't beat that.

Two clowns were nailing new sides on to one of the train carriages. One of them kept throwing nails away.

'What are you doing?' asked the other clown.

'They've all got the points at the wrong end.'

'Don't be silly! We can use them for the other side of the carriage.'

Knock knock!
Who's there?
Alex.
Alex who?
Alex the questions round here!

Knock knock!
Who's there?
Mort.
Mort who?
Mort to the point, who are you?

Knock knock!
Who's there?
Melman.
Melman who?
Melman with your letters. Do you want them or not?

Knock knock!
Who's there?
Julien.
Julien who?
Julien forwards and open the door, please.

Knock knock!
Who's there?
Sonya.
Sonya who?
Sonya shoe? I can smell it from here!

Knock knock!
Who's there?
Phil.
Phil who?
Phil up my hot water bottle, I'm cold!

Knock Knock!
Who's there?
Freddie the Interrupting Dog.
Freddie the int—
WOOF!

Knock knock!
Who's there?
Ellie.
Ellie who?
Ellie Phants never forget!

83

SENSATIONAL SONYA
THE BICYCLING BEAR

Why is Sonya big, hairy and brown?
Because if she was small, smooth and white she'd be an egg.

Sonya always rides her bike twice. She's good at recycling.

Julien first met Sonya when she knocked him down some stairs.
He fell head over heels in love.

Sonya thought her bike was haunted. So she took the spooks off.

Julien: 'Wow, I just saw Sonya doing that trick where she rides along on just the back wheel!'

Maurice: 'Wheelie?'

Julien: 'Of course, I wouldn't make that up.'

Why can't Sonya's bike stand up on it's own? Because it's two-tyred.

Alex was annoyed when Sonya ran into him on her bike.

'I thought she knew how to ride that thing!' he grumbled.

'She does,' Gia explained. 'But she hasn't learned how to ring the bell yet.'

What did Sonya find was the hardest thing about learning to ride a bike? The ground.

Sonya took Julien for a ride on the back of her bike, and ended up going the wrong way down a one-way street.

'I don't know where you're going, darling,' said Julien. 'But I think we're too late – everyone else is coming back.'

MAGNIFICENT MARTY

How does Marty impersonate an elk?
He puts on a false moose-tache.

'For my next trick,' said Marty,
'I will eat a percussion instrument in a bap . . .
Drum roll, please!'

Marty really went for it when
he drove through Monaco, but he
knocked over lots of road signs.
He pulled out all the stops.

As Marty swerved down the one-way street,
a driver coming the other way flashed
his lights and yelled out of his window,
'You're going the wrong way!'
 'That's odd,' thought Marty. 'How does he
know where we're going?'

Marty loved driving in Monaco – though his passengers weren't quite as happy. Here's all he knows about the Highway Code.

Keep the steering wheel in front of you

Hey, humans! Wave and smile, guys!

Watch out for Gloria and Julien on a flying bike

What, they're throwing spears? Tough crowd

Some guy's putting up an umbrella – it's going to rain

Is that me? I must be going the right way!

AMAZING ALEX

What do you call a lion with a toothache?
Rory.

Sometimes Alex likes an undercooked steak, but not often.
It's rare.

What did Alex say to his bone?
'It's been nice gnawing you!'

Where does Alex buy stuff?
He goes on-lion – his favourite site is ePrey.

Alex likes formal dances where they serve steak.
Yes, he loves meatballs.

ALEX BREATHED IN HELIUM FROM A BUNCH OF BALLOONS. HE STARTED AN UP-ROAR.

Alex is glad Nana hasn't come to see the circus. He's frightened of that itty-bitty kitty hitter.

Why does it take Alex so long to watch a DVD? **He keeps on pressing 'Paws'.**

Alex has been learning to limbo dance. He's pretty good – he can get under a rug now.

PENGUIN PRANKS

What's black and white, black and white, black and white and black and white?
Private rolling down a hill.

'Kowalski, I'm not sure you should be trying to fix that computer.'
'Don't worry, in the whole time I've been doing this, I've only ever made one computer blow up.'
'Wow. So how many computers have you fixed?'
'This will be the second.'

Rico took ages trying to work out how to fit his seatbelt.
Then suddenly, it clicked.

Skipper walked into a fishmongers with a huge salmon under his flipper.
'Do you make fishcakes?' he asked.
'Of course,' replied the fishmonger.
'Oh good,' said Skipper. 'Can you make one for Billy here? It's his birthday.'

The other Penguins say that Private always contradicts them, but he disagrees.

There's one place in Monaco that Rico can't stand. **It's a slippery bit of pavement near the casino.**

IF KOWALSKI TELLS RICO TO DO ONE MORE SOMERSAULT, HE'S GOING TO FLIP.

'OK, Kowalski – think of a number. Add twenty. Take away three. Multiply by ten. Now close your eyes. Done that?'
   'Yes, Skipper.'
   'Dark, isn't it?'

The Penguins were flying their plane and searching desperately for somewhere to land.
   'Look, Skipper! A runway!' yelled Private.
   They landed with a bump, and screeched to a halt right at the edge of the runway.
   'That was close!' said Skipper. 'Wow, this runway is incredibly short!'
   'Yeah . . .' said Kowalski, looking around. 'And **ridiculously** wide.'

EVERYTHING SKIPPER KNOWS ABOUT FLYING

All take-offs are optional.
Every landing is compulsory.

Flying isn't dangerous.
Crashing is dangerous.

The only time you can have too much fuel
is when your plane is on fire.

A good landing is when you can walk
away afterwards. A great landing is when
the plane can be used again.

Gravity isn't one of those laws
you might get away with breaking.

There are old pilots
and pilots that take risks.
There are no old pilots that take risks.

If all you can see is the ground spinning
round, and all you can hear is
passengers screaming . . .
something may have gone wrong.

All pilots start with a bag full of luck
and an empty bag of experience.
The trick is to fill the bag of experience
before the bag of luck runs out.

Page 12 – Sort the Silhouette: D is the right shadow.

Page 13 – Animal Anagrams: ELEPHANT, TIGER, JAGUAR, CHIMPANZEE, SEALION, BEAR, HIPPOPOTAMUS, ZEBRA, GIRAFFE, LEMUR.

Page 24 – Spot the Difference:

Page 30 – Odd Animal Out: Stefano – C (smaller feet); Gloria – A (ball is missing a star); Alex – D (juggling balls in different order); Melman – B (tail is missing).

Page 38 – What's My Name?:

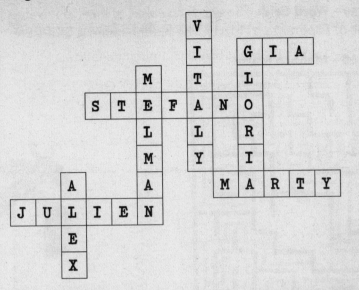

Page 46 – Pick a Penguin: Kowalski is the only one helping.

Page 52 – Wacky Wordsearch:

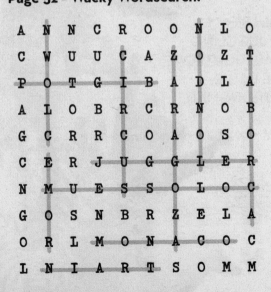

```
A N N C R O O N L O
C W U U C A Z O Z T
P O T G I B A D L A
A L O B R C R N O B
G C R R C O A O S O
C E R J U G G L E R
N M U E S S O L O C
G O S N B R Z E L A
O R L M O N A C O C
L N I A R T S O M M
```

95

Page 58 – Join the Dots: Marty is in a cannon.

Page 59 – Word Grid: 1) Sonya, 2) Kowalski, 3) Rico, 4) Private, 5) Phil, 6) Esperanza, 7) Marty. The hidden name is SKIPPER.

Page 68 – Monaco Maze:

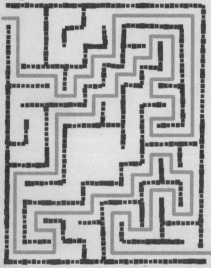

Page 69 – Pick a Pair: BIG TOP, SAFETY NET, JUGGLING BALL, TRAPEZE BAR, TIGHTROPE, RINGMASTER, FIRE EATER, DANCING DOG, STRONGMAN, KNIFE THROWER.

Page 74 – Jigsaw Juggle: A - 5, B - 1, C - 3, D - 2, E - 6. Piece 4 is not from this jigsaw.